MANDRAKE
the MAGICIAN

**by LEE FALK
and
PHIL DAVIS**

MANDRAKE
IN
HOLLYWOOD

NOSTALGIA PRESS, BOX 293, FRANKLIN SQUARE, N.Y. 11010

Edited by Maurice Horn
Book Design by Maurice Horn
Layout & Production by Sid Hassin & Joseph Goteri

Library of Congress Catalog Card Number 76-159555

INTRODUCTION

PHIL DAVIS

Upon his graduation from the University of Illinois in 1933, Lee Falk started in life with a fistful of short stories, a couple of stage plays and two weeks of continuity for a new comic-strip that he had created along with a fellow Missourian, Phil Davis. Leaving Saint-Louis for New York, the would-be writer made the rounds of publishers, stage producers, and syndicates, having decided to devote his talents to whichever of his projects would sell first. Trying his luck, Falk submitted his comic-strip idea to King Features Syndicate, which quickly grabbed it...and that's how "Mandrake the Magician" was born this eleventh of June 1934.

Starting as a daily feature, "Mandrake" met with immediate success, and before long the syndicate had decided to run the series as a Sunday page as well (February, 1935). Mandrake's fame has grown ever since and, as a straight adventure-type strip, it has proved, over the years, second in popularity only to Falk's other brainchild, the Phantom. Its success can be measured by the host of imitators to which our magician gave rise in the forties and fifties, mostly in comic-books...and by the fact that after all these years, "Mandrake" is still among the top features in its category.

As a child, Lee Falk had always been fascinated by magicians. Going to the circus with his father, he would volunteer to play foil to such masters as Thornston or Cardini. Mandrake was born of this enchantment, and with his red cape, his hat, the ritualism of his gestures, he is the synthesis of all the magicians Lee Falk had seen, and the magician that perhaps he dreamt one day to become.

It is interesting to note that physically Mandrake with his dark, neatly parted hair and his trim moustache was modelled after Lee Falk himself. Rather dull and one-dimensional at first, our hero will become more and more complex and human. At the beginning of the series, Mandrake will be a real wizard, endowed with supernatural powers but little by little he will be made more believable (and also more lovable). As a master of hypnotism and legerdemain (to which he was initiated in Tibet), Mandrake is just a mortal, and to triumph over his enemies, he disposes only of his superior faculties of intelligence, resourcefulness and courage.

In the course of his exploits, Mandrake is forever flanked by his faithful companion Lothar, king of a faraway African tribe, whose Herculean strength often wins the day, when Mandrake's magic has failed.

No hero's life would be complete without a sweetheart, and Mandrake met his match in the person of Princess Narda (Falk seems to have a thing for royalty) who tried to do him in on several occasions (ah love!) before settling into what seems to have become a morganatic marriage of sorts.

Mandrake's adventures take place on the four corners of the earth, and very often outside of it as well (journeys to the moon, to the galaxies, etc.); unlike the Phantom, he has no base from where he operates, no familiar decor which at once situates him. He has to create his own universe and this he does with his powers of illusion, which brings "Mandrake" closer to modern intellectual currents than any other adventure strip.

Lee Falk's scenarios are very imaginative, very elaborate; the plots twist and turn, like in a good stage play and they are as varied in tone as in setting. From straight adventure, they will veer to science-fiction, or to the mystery-story, the fantastic tale, even the humorous anecdote. The dialogue is brisk and witty, bringing to mind the playwright Lee Falk had always wanted to be (and was later to become).

One cannot write about "Mandrake" without mentioning the man who, for more than thirty years, brought to the strip his distinctive talent, his clarity of style and the nonchalant yet achieved line of his elegant pen: Phil Davis. A native of Saint-Louis, Davis had achieved some measure of success as a commercial artist before meeting Lee Falk. Davis's uncanny ability in creating subtle moods and tonalities with a few simple lines, just the right placement of objects and characters, and a touch of shading, has earned him the admiration of many artists and film-makers, among whom can be found Alain Resnais and Federico Fellini. At Phil Davis's death in 1965, the strip was taken over by Fredericks.

The two adventures which make up "Mandrake in Hollywood" were first published in daily form from January, 31 through July 9, 1938, at a time when the strip was at a high point in its career. In these stories, you will enjoy Falk's imaginativeness, his wit and literary qualities, and Davis's clever drawing, beautiful line and fine understatement, as well as the subtle but very definite interplay between the artist and the writer that gives the strip its unique flavor.

Maurice C. Horn

MANDRAKE IS EN ROUTE TO HOLLYWOOD—

MANDRAKE, THE STUDIO'S ARRANGED A PARTY FOR YOU AT THE STATION. COULD YOU DO SOMETHING SPECTACULAR WHEN WE ARRIVE--AS AN ENTRANCE, YOU KNOW?

SPECTACULAR?

HOW'S THIS?

UH-- NEVER--MIND-- WE'D BETTER --SKIP IT--

SAY, LOTHAR, ISN'T IT SORTA SCARY, WORKING FOR A MAN LIKE MANDRAKE?

SCARY? HIM WOULDN'T HURT NO FELLOW. IS NICEST MAN IN WORLD.

SAY, FOR EXAMPLE, HIM WOULD TURN BAD FELLOW INTO CIGARETTE-LIGHTER --BUT WOULDN'T REALLY HURT HIM.

YEAH? GUESS I BETTER STICK TO MATCHES! MAY LIGHT MY CIGARETTE WITH MY BEST FRIEND, AND NOT KNOW IT!

HOLLYWOOD
:
IN THE
FLITCH
&
SNORK
STUDIOS.

MANDRAKE WILL BE HERE SOON AND HIS CONTRACT IS ALL READY FOR HIM.

YES--BUT WHAT IF HE READS IT THROUGH, FLITCH?

NOBODY EVER READS ALL THOSE PARAGRAPHS OF SMALL PRINT.

AND EVEN IF HE DOES FIND **THE** PARAGRAPH, IT'S WRITTEN SO IT'D FOOL EVEN A LAWYER AT FIRST SIGHT.

tomorrow--THE RUSH ACT

TOMORROW-- THAT FELLOW IN CHINA --

A TALKING PEN AND A TALKING CONTRACT "SAVE" MANDRAKE FROM FLITCH & SNORK'S CROOKED PLAN.

I WON'T SIGN A CROOKED CONTRACT!

I CAN'T HELP IT IF I'M CROOKED. IT'S THE WAY I'M MADE.

THIS SEEMS TO BE THE HIDDEN PARAGRAPH IN QUESTION. *Hmm*—ACCORDING TO THIS, THE SALARY YOU AGREED TO PAY ME DOESN'T MEAN A THING. YOU CAN CUT IT TO ANYTHING YOU LIKE.

IT WAS HIS IDEA!

IT WAS HIS IDEA. JUST A JOKE. MANDRAKE, WE'LL DOUBLE YOUR SALARY! WE'LL WRITE YOU A NEW CONTRACT!

NO, THANK YOU, **GENTLEMEN.** I'VE NEVER BEEN A GLUTTON ABOUT MONEY, BUT I CAN'T WORK WITH PEOPLE I CAN'T TRUST.

YOU CAN'T WALK OUT ON US! WE'LL SEE YOU'RE BARRED FROM EVERY MAJOR STUDIO IN HOLLYWOOD!

UNFORTUNATELY, FLEMING, OVER AT GRANITE STUDIOS, MADE ME AN OFFER. AT THE TIME YOUR CONTRACT SEEMED BETTER. GOODBYE.

YOU AND YOUR IDEAS! THERE HE GOES! HE'D BEEN WORTH MILLIONS TO US!

IT WAS THIS BLAMED PEN THAT SPILLED THE BEANS! SAY-- WERE WE HEARING THINGS--?

TOMORROW— SCREEN TEST

MANDRAKE'S SCREEN TEST.

NOW--YOU'RE IN LOVE WITH THIS GIRL, MANDRAKE. YOU HAVEN'T SEEN HER FOR MONTHS! YOU COME IN THE ROOM--AND GIVE HER A BIG KISS! OKAY--LET'S TRY IT.

NAW--NAW--NOT THAT WAY! YOU'VE GOT TO PUT SOME FEELING INTO IT. MAKE IT LOOK LIKE YOU MEANT IT! NOW--LET'S TRY IT AGAIN-- AND MAKE IT HOT!

FLAMES!! WHAT--THE--!

R-10

NOW, MANDRAKE, I WANT YOU TO DO ONE OF YOUR TRICKS FOR THE CAMERA.

I'M AFRAID I CAN'T FOOL THE CAMERA WITHOUT TRICK APPARATUS.

YOU SEE, MUCH OF MY MAGIC IS BASED ON HYPNOTISM.

BUT I'VE SEEN YOU TURN A MOUSE INTO AN ELEPHANT AND-- DO YOU MEAN TO SAY YOU CAN HYPNOTIZE A WHOLE ROOMFUL OF PEOPLE---

R-11

tomorrow—PROOF

Copr. 1938, King Features Syndicate, Inc., World rights reserved

Monday—WHAT THE CAMERA SAW

MANDRAKE SAYS HE CAN'T HYPNOTIZE A CAMERA. TO ILLUSTRATE HIS POINT, THE FOLLOWING TEST IS MADE IN GRANITE STUDIOS.

TWENTY PEOPLE SEE MANDRAKE MOUNT A HORSE, AFTER MAKING IT APPEAR FROM NOWHERE, AND THE MOVIE CAMERA TAKES THE SCENE!

BUT THE DEVELOPED FILM SHOWS THAT MANDRAKE **REALLY** ONLY LIT A CIGARETTE AND SAT ON A CHAIR!

HOW DID YOU DO IT? EVERYBODY ON THE SET SWORE THEY SAW YOU GET ON THAT HORSE! YOU CALL IT MASS HYPNOTISM! I CALL IT BLACK MAGIC!

WHAT'S IN A NAME?

JUST A FEW MORE "STILLS," MANDRAKE, AND THEN WE'LL LET YOU GO FOR THE DAY. HOW ABOUT A BIG SMILE?

MY UPPER LIP INFORMS ME THAT IT REFUSES TO SMILE ANY MORE. IT'S ABSOLUTELY WORN OUT.

FINISHED NOW?

FINISHED IS THE WORD, LOTHAR. AFTER WE LEAVE HOLLYWOOD, I'LL GET A JOB AS A PIANO-MOVER, AND HAVE A GOOD REST. LOOK AT THAT FELLOW!

AHEAD, A MAN SUDDENLY DASHES OUT OF THE BUSHES--

--AND RUNS DIRECTLY IN THE PATH OF AN AUTOMOBILE!

R-15

MANDRAKE SEES A MAN DASH DIRECTLY INTO THE PATH OF AN AUTOMOBILE! THE CAR SWERVES --MISSING THE MAN---

BUT THE MAN COLLAPSES ON THE ROAD--

CALL A DOCTOR! THE POOR MAN --HE'S LYING-- SO STILL --!

WHY--THAT'S MARILYN DAWN, THE GIRL WHO HELPED ME IN MY SCREEN TEST! HER CAR DIDN'T HIT THAT MAN--THOUGH HE DID HIS BEST TO HIT IT!

MAN TRY TO RUN OVER CAR? SOUND SILLY.

R-16

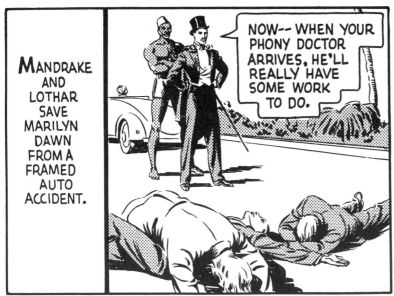

MANDRAKE AND LOTHAR SAVE MARILYN DAWN FROM A FRAMED AUTO ACCIDENT.

NOW-- WHEN YOUR PHONY DOCTOR ARRIVES, HE'LL REALLY HAVE SOME WORK TO DO.

YOU UNDERSTAND, MARILYN, THAT THESE MEN FRAMED THE ACCIDENT-- HOPING TO COLLECT HUGE DAMAGES FROM YOU OR THE STUDIO.

IF MY CAR SCRATCHES THE FENDER OF ANOTHER CAR, THE OWNER SUES ME FOR TWICE THE VALUE OF THE CAR.

IF A DELIVERY BOY STUBS HIS TOE ON MY STAIRS, I'M SUED FOR A YEAR'S HOSPITAL BILL, MENTAL SHOCK AND CRIMINAL NEGLIGENCE. I'M NOT STINGY ABOUT MONEY, BUT---

YOU'RE A GREAT STAR, MARILYN. THAT'S THE PENALTY OF FAME.

I KNOW, MANDRAKE. THAT'S ONE REASON WHY I WEAR TWO FACES.

R-R1

tomorrow— TWO FACES?

MARILYN, YOU SAID YOU WEAR TWO FACES. WHAT DO YOU MEAN BY THAT?

OH, JUST A LITTLE EXPRESSION OF MINE.-DOESN'T REALLY MEAN ANYTHING.

FLEMING HAS GREAT HOPES FOR YOU, MANDRAKE. HE SAID THAT IF YOUR FIRST PICTURE IS WELL-RECEIVED, YOU'LL BE MY LEADING MAN IN MY NEXT PICTURE.

I'M AFRAID THAT'S THE WRONG END OF THE LADDER. I DON'T WANT TO START AT THE TOP -- AND CLIMB DOWN.

tomorrow - DON'T MIND ME

TOMORROW — TWO FACES —

tomorrow — NETTIE BROODS

TOMORROW — NETTIE AND FARRELL PLOT!

WHAT YOU SUGGEST IS IMPOSSIBLE. NETTIE!

WHY, FARRELL? I'VE DOUBLED FOR MARILYN DAWN SO LONG THAT I CAN BE HER! HER VOICE--HER HANDWRITING--I CAN DO IT ALL! WE LOOK SO EXACTLY ALIKE THAT YOU--HER MANAGER, CAN HARDLY TELL US APART!

YOU'RE ONLY GETTING TEN PER CENT OF MARILYN'S SALARY! IF I BECOME MARILYN DAWN--YOU'LL GET FIFTY PER CENT! WE CAN'T MISS! HER FRIENDS--THE STUDIO--THEY'VE SEEN MORE OF ME THAN OF HER!

YOU'RE FORGETTING THAT MARILYN DAWN IS A GREAT ACTRESS. CAN YOU FOOL THE PUBLIC, TOO?

GREAT ACTRESS, BOSH! I CAME HERE TO BE AN ACTRESS. I'VE HAD STAGE EXPERIENCE! I CAN ACT CIRCLES AROUND HER.

YOU'RE THE ONLY ONE THAT KNOWS SHE HAS A DOUBLE! IS IT WORTH FIFTY PER CENT OF HER SALARY?

BY GEORGE. I THINK WE CAN DO IT! IN FACT, THE MORE I THINK OF IT, THE EASIER IT LOOKS!

MARILYN, I CAN'T FIGURE YOU OUT. SOME DAYS, YOU SEEM LIKE AN ENTIRELY DIFFERENT PERSON.

REALLY, MANDRAKE, AND WHICH PERSON DO YOU PREFER?

I PREFER YOU THE WAY YOU ARE NOW, MARILYN.

I'M GOING AWAY ON A LITTLE VACATION. WHEN I COME BACK I'LL EXPLAIN THE MYSTERY TO YOU, I PROMISE. AND--AND I'M GLAD YOU LIKE ME--THE WAY I AM NOW.

tomorrow – MARILYN RETURNS

3-4

3-5

Continued –

NETTIE AND FARRELL'S PLOT BEGINS, AS MARILYN IS LOCKED OUT OF HER OWN HOUSE!

LIZA, YOU SILLY FOOL, I'M MARILYN DAWN!

NOW, MISS NETTIE, I'VE TRIED TO BE NICE TO YOU --- BUT MISS DAWN FIRED YOU AND YOU **CAN'T** COME IN!

MISS DAWN SAID SHE'D PROBABLY HAVE TROUBLE WITH YOU. THAT'S WHY I'M HERE. GIVE ME THE KEYS TO THAT CAR.

THE -- THE KEYS --?

THANK YOU. THAT CAR BELONGS TO MISS DAWN. NOW IF YOU WANT TO STAY OUT OF TROUBLE, YOU'LL LEAVE HERE AND STOP BOTHERING MISS DAWN.

BUT I -- I'M -- THIS IS MY HOUSE. I'M --

I'M MARILYN DAWN! I TRIED TO DRAW SOME MONEY FROM MY ACCOUNT AND --

OH, YES. PLEASE COME WITH ME.

MISS DAWN WARNED US ABOUT YOU. SAID YOU WERE HER DOUBLE -- THAT SHE'D FIRED YOU -- AND THAT YOU'D PROBABLY TRY TO STEAL MONEY FROM HER ACCOUNT!

STEAL! IT'S MY MONEY! LET ME SHOW YOU MY SIGNATURE!

NETTIE AND FARRELL'S PLOT HAS WORKED. NETTIE, FORMERLY MARILYN DAWN'S DOUBLE, HAS TAKEN MARILYN'S PLACE!

I THINK IT'S A SHAME TO TURN THAT GIRL OUT, MARILYN. THE RESEMBLANCE IS AMAZING. WE COULD USE HER AS A STAND-IN FOR YOU.

NO! I WON'T HAVE HER AROUND!

SO THIS IS WHY YOU ALWAYS SEEMED SO CHANGEABLE, MARILYN. YOU WERE REALLY TWO PEOPLE.

YES, MANDRAKE, BUT THAT'S OVER NOW. NETTIE BECAME A NUISANCE.

WELL--WHOM WAS I DANCING WITH THE OTHER NIGHT? YOU --OR NETTIE?

NETTIE, OF COURSE.

BUT NOW THAT WE'RE GOING TO BE IN THE SAME PICTURE TOGETHER-- PERHAPS YOU AND I SHOULD BECOME BETTER ACQUAINTED.

3-10

I'M MARILYN DAWN. I'VE GOT TO GET IN TO SEE MR. FLEMING!

WE KNOW ALL ABOUT YOU, NETTIE. THAT GAG WON'T WORK ANY-MORE. YOU CAN'T GET IN!

3-11

I'VE GOT A WARRANT HERE FOR YOU, MISS DAWN. SOME GIRL CLAIMS SHE'S YOU -- AND CHARGES YOU WITH IMPERSONATION AND EMBEZZLEMENT.

WILL I NEVER BE RID OF THAT NETTIE?

OF COURSE, I READ ALL ABOUT THAT DOUBLE IN THE PAPERS, BUT SHE STILL CLAIMS SHE'S MISS DAWN.

YOU KNOW HOW IT IS. MOVIE STARS ARE ALWAYS ANNOYED BY CRANKS LIKE THAT.

I'M SURE YOU CAN QUASH THIS CASE. YOU WON'T HAVE TO APPEAR IN COURT. COULD I -- GET MISS DAWN'S AUTOGRAPH?

MISS DAWN WILL BE GLAD TO GIVE YOU HER PERSONAL AUTOGRAPH.

NOW -- IT MAKES NO DIFFERENCE TO ME THAT YOU WEREN'T THE REAL MARILYN DAWN, BUT, NETTIE -- I WISH YOU'D TOLD ME.

MANDRAKE -- WON'T YOU BELIEVE ME? I -- AM -- MARILYN -- DAWN!

PLEASE, NETTIE. I KNOW IT WAS YOUR JOB TO IMPERSONATE MARILYN. IT'S QUITE ALL RIGHT. I UNDERSTAND.

MANDRAKE -- NO ONE BELIEVES ME, NOT EVEN YOU. THIS IS A NIGHTMARE -- IT CAN'T GO ON ---

I CAN'T GET INTO MY OWN HOME. MY OWN STUDIO -- MY OWN BANK ACCOUNT IS CLOSED TO ME -- I'M PENNILESS -- I -- I DON'T KNOW WHAT TO DO NEXT ---

STRANGE THING, LOTHAR. SHE'S BEEN PLAYING THE PART OF MARILYN SO LONG, THAT I'M CONVINCED SHE REALLY THINKS SHE IS MARILYN!

3-12

Next Week = FLY IN THE OINTMENT —

NETTIE, FORMERLY MARILYN DAWN'S DOUBLE. HAS TAKEN MARILYN'S PLACE!

HERE'S YOUR CUT FOR THE WEEK, NETTIE. IT'S GOING MARVELOUSLY! EVERYBODY THINKS YOU'RE MARILYN DAWN!

WHY SHOULDN'T THEY? THEY USED TO SEE MORE OF ME THAN THEY DID OF HER. AND WE LOOK EXACTLY ALIKE.

3·14

HOW I USED TO HATE HER --WITH HER AIRS AND UPPITY MANNERS!

NOW, NETTIE. SHE IS DOWN. WHY KICK HER? AFTER ALL, SHE WAS A NICE GIRL.

NETTIE, SINCE YOU AND I ARE PARTNERS--IN A PERFECT CRIME-- WE SHOULD GET TO KNOW EACH OTHER BETTER---

DON'T CALL ME NETTIE! I'M MARILYN-- FROM NOW ON.

AND REMEMBER THIS, FARRELL. THIS IS STRICTLY A BUSINESS ARRANGEMENT. I'VE ALREADY GOT A SWEETHEART. HIS NAME IS D-O-U-G-H --AND I GO FOR HIM IN A BIG WAY!

OKAY-- NETTIE.

THAT'S AN EXQUISITE THING, MISS DAWN.

YES--BUT SHOW ME SOMETHING WITH MORE DASH.

I'LL TAKE THE THREE DIAMOND BRACELETS, THE PEARLS--AND THAT STAR SAPPHIRE RING.

YES, MISS DAWN!

3·15

3-16

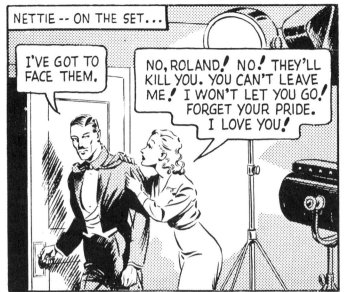

NETTIE -- ON THE SET...

I'VE GOT TO FACE THEM.

NO, ROLAND! NO! THEY'LL KILL YOU. YOU CAN'T LEAVE ME! I WON'T LET YOU GO! FORGET YOUR PRIDE. I LOVE YOU!

WE'LL HAVE TO SHOOT THAT AGAIN. WHAT'S THE MATTER, MARILYN? DON'T YOU FEEL WELL, TODAY?

I DON'T KNOW WHAT YOU MEAN! I'M DOING ALL RIGHT!

MY GOSH--I'VE NEVER SEEN DAWN SO BAD. WHAT'S THE MATTER WITH HER?

SOUNDS LIKE AMATEUR NIGHT.

3-17

I USED TO MISS MY BREAKFAST SO I COULD BE ON TIME TO HEAR HER REHEARSE HER SCENES!

YEAH? WELL, BRING YOUR EGGS WITH YOU AND SCRAMBLE 'EM ON. HER HEAD. SHE'S TURNING IN- TO A PLAIN HAM!

Copr. 1938, King Features Syndicate, Inc. World rights reserved

NOW, MR. FLEMING --ABOUT MARILYN DAWN'S NEW CONTRACT--

YES--WE'LL HAVE TO WAIT UNTIL THIS NEW PICTURE IS FINISHED, FARRELL. I'VE BEEN HEARING SOME UNPLEASANT THINGS ABOUT HER.

THAT'S RIDICULOUS. MARILYN DAWN IS THE GREATEST BOX-OFFICE ATTRACTION IN THE BUSINESS!

YES--UP TO NOW, BUT IF THINGS GO ON AS THEY ARE-- SHE MAY NOT BE ABLE TO EARN HER PRESENT HIGH SALARY.

I THOUGHT YOU COULD ACT, NETTIE! EVERYBODY AROUND THE STUDIO IS TALKING. YOU'RE A FLOP! WHAT HAVE I GOTTEN MYSELF INTO?

DON'T BE SILLY, FARRELL. PETTY STUDIO JEALOUSY --THAT'S ALL.

YEAH? FLEMING'S GOING TO CUT YOUR SALARY. THEN--THERE'LL BE NO SALARY! MAYBE I SHOULDA STUCK WITH THE **REAL MARILYN**--SHE WAS A REAL STAR!

OH--YOU'LL KEEP QUIET! WE'RE IN THIS TOGETHER! IF WE'RE FOUND OUT---WE'LL GO TO JAIL TOGETHER!

As MANDRAKE ENTERTAINS THE CREW ON THE SET--

I'M GETTING TIRED OF BEING TALKED AT! HOW ABOUT YOU?

AW--IT'S ALWAYS THE SAME OLD GRIND WITH ME.

MANDRAKE-- MR. FLEMING WANTS YOU IN THE PROJECTION-ROOM.

3-19

THIS PICTURE LOOKS SOUR TO ME, MANDRAKE.

IT'S MARILYN. SHE LOOKS THE SAME, SOUNDS THE SAME--BUT SHE'S ACTING LIKE A NOVICE! MY GREATEST STAR! I CAN'T UNDERSTAND IT!

HMM--VERY STRANGE, MR. FLEMING --VERY STRANGE--PERHAPS--

IS MANDRAKE BEGINNING TO SUSPECT THE TRUTH?

UNKNOWN FAN! HUH! DOES SHE THINK SHE CAN SCARE ME? WHY DOESN'T SHE HIRE A GHOST TO DO HER HAUNTING?

SHE'S GOING TO BE A HARD NUT TO CRACK. SHE'S COLD AND RELENTLESS. I HOPED WE COULD SHAKE HER ENOUGH TO MAKE HER LOSE CONFIDENCE -- AND CONFESS EVERYTHING. I'LL TRY AGAIN -- TOMORROW --

NETTIE NETTIE

tomorrow - HYPNOTISM

MANDRAKE DINES WITH NETTIE --WHO POSES AS MARILYN DAWN =

MY GOODNESS -- WHY, SHE --

THANK YOU.

3-26

THAT CIGARETTE GIRL-- LOOKED JUST LIKE ME --AND LOOK-- THAT WOMAN!

WHY, MARILYN, THERE'S NOT THE SLIGHTEST RESEMBLANCE.

CHECK ROOM

AND THAT CHECK GIRL -- OH, I'M JUST SEEING THINGS. THEY'VE PROBABLY SEEN ME IN PICTURES-- AND ARE TRYING TO MAKE UP LIKE ME.

WELL -- THAT DIDN'T WORK. SHE'S TOUGH. WE'LL HAVE TO WAIT FOR THE UNEXPECTED.

Continued.

3-31

POSING AS A FICTITIOUS UNCLE OF MARILYN DAWN, MANDRAKE REVEALS THE HOAX AT LAST!

GO BACK!

NOW, FARRELL AND NETTIE --THE JIG IS UP-- AND YOUR CLEVER HOAX IS OVER. YOU'LL HAVE PLENTY OF TIME IN PRISON TO FIGURE OUT HOW YOU COULD HAVE AVOIDED THIS SHOW-DOWN!

4-1

HAVE A GOOD CRY, MARILYN. YOUR NIGHTMARE IS OVER. FARRELL AND NETTIE ARE IN JAIL--AND THEIR NIGHTMARE IS JUST BEGINNING. EMBEZZLEMENT-- AND A FEW OTHER THINGS.

BUT HOW THAT NETTIE GIRL COULD HAVE FOOLED **ME** INTO THINKING SHE WAS YOU--

WE WERE ALL FOOLED FOR A WHILE, BUT IT'S ALL OVER NOW.

AND I'M MYSELF AGAIN -- AND I CAN GO BACK TO WORK ON THE SET! NO MORE DOUBLES FOR ME! MANDRAKE-- HOW CAN I---

THANK ME? JUST BY BEING YOURSELF. DOING A PICTURE WITH YOU INSTEAD OF NETTIE-- WILL BE MY REWARD--

4-2

YOU GOT ME INTO THIS-- YOU--YOU--

I WANT TO GO TO ANOTHER JAIL! I WON'T BE IN THE SAME JAIL WITH YOU!

AND FARRELL'S AND NETTIE'S GREAT HOAX ENDS--BEHINDS BARS INSTEAD OF FOOTLIGHTS!

IT'S SO GOOD TO GET BACK TO WORK AGAIN, MANDRAKE. THE OLD STUDIO CAFETERIA IS THE SAME AS EVER.

WHAT LOOKS GOOD TO YOU, MARILYN?

EVERYTHING LOOKS GOOD --OH, DEAR, THIS TRAY IS GETTING SO HEAVY AND HARD TO MANAGE --

MAYBE I CAN HELP YOU --

MANDRAKE GESTURES AND THE TRAY FLOATS ALONG AT MARILYN'S SIDE . . .

THIS IS WHAT I CALL SERVICE!

4-4

I TOLD THEM I DIDN'T LIKE THAT KIND OF SAUCE ON THE ASPARAGUS --

NOW, SONNY--

MANDRAKE GESTURES AND THE PLATE BOUNCES BACK UP ON THE TABLE BEFORE IT'S HAD A CHANCE TO HIT THE FLOOR--!

HERE, HERE, YOUNG MAN, THAT'LL NEVER DO!

tomorrow - MORE ABOUT SONNY

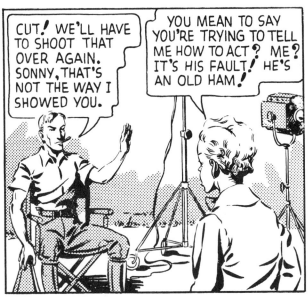

tomorrow--GEORGE

WILL SONNY, CINEMA IDOL OF MILLIONS, BE KIDNAPPED?

STILL NO WORD FROM THE KIDNAPPERS, MANDRAKE.?

NO, AND NOT A SINGLE CLUE, BUT EVERYONE'S WORKING HARD, FLEMING. WE'LL FIND SONNY.

MY SCRAMBLED EGGS ARE ALWAYS FLAVORED WITH CHEESE. I CAN'T EAT THESE EGGS. TAKE THEM AWAY.

SAY-- WHAT IS THIS?

CAN'T THAT KID EAT WHAT THE REST OF US EAT? WHAT'S HE THINK THIS IS -- A HOTEL?

SONNY'S WORTH A MILLION BUCKS TO US, BUD, SO IF HE WANTS CHEESE WITH HIS EGGS -- GIVE HIM CHEESE.

5-2   Copr 1938, King Features Syndicate Inc World rights reserved

CHEESE ? SAY-- DID WE KIDNAP HIM OR DID HE KIDNAP US?

MY TROUSERS HAVEN'T BEEN PRESSED. I'M USED TO PRESSED TROUSERS EVERYDAY!

WELL, AIN'T THAT TOO BAD?

PRESS 'EM, BUD.

SAY-- THIS KID'S DRIVING ME CRAZY! PETE -- I JUST HAD A HORRIBLE THOUGHT! SUPPOS'N THEY WON'T PAY A RANSOM FOR HIM ---

World rights reserved
Copr. 1938, King Features Syndicate, Inc.

--AND WE'RE STUCK WITH HIM FOR THE REST OF OUR LIVES!

AW--BE YOURSELF, BUD.

I'VE HAD ENOUGH OF THIS NURSE-MAID STUFF! LISTEN, BRAT, DON'T GIVE ME NO MORE OF YOUR LIP OR I'LL SLAP YOU DOWN! SEE?

Y-YES, SIR.

5-3

PETE, HOW WE GONNA CONTACT SONNY'S FOLKS FOR THE RANSOM? THEIR HOUSE IS WATCHED NIGHT AND DAY.

YEAH, AND THE TELEPHONE'S TAPPED --AND I DON'T WANT TO USE THE MAILS AND HAVE ANY LETTERS FOR THEM EXPERTS TO GO OVER.

GEORGE, YOU WAS SONNY'S VALET. HAS THE KID GOT ANY SPECIAL FRIENDS WE COULD APPROACH --AS A GO-BETWEEN?

SONNY WAS TOO SNOOTY TO BE POPULAR WITH ANYBODY--EXCEPT --LEMME SEE-- HE SORTA TOOK A LIKING TO MANDRAKE.

MANDRAKE-- THAT'S THE FELLA WE'LL APPROACH, BUT WHO'S GONNA CONTACT HIM? NOT ME!

YEAH--WE GOTTA FIND SOMEBODY ELSE. THEY TELL ME HE'S A PRETTY TRICKY GUY. SAY--BUD, LOOK--OUT THERE!

WHITEY AND TWO OF THE KIDS FROM SONNY'S NEIGHBORHOOD ARE OUT FOR A HIKE.

5-4

WELL, YOU FOUND US, ALL RIGHT.

THE KID'S A SCRAPPER. HOLD HIM WHILE I GET THIS BLINDFOLD ON HIM.

5-6

WE'LL DRIVE AROUND IN A CIRCLE FOR A COUPLA HOURS -- SO HE WON'T KNOW WHERE OUR HIDE-OUT IS.

TOMORROW -- REUNION

WHITEY IS BROUGHT TO THE HIDE-OUT WHERE SONNY IS HELD. THE KIDNAPPERS PLAN TO USE WHITEY TO CONTACT MANDRAKE.

GEE -- SONNY! ARE YOU OKAY? EVERYBODY IN THE COUNTRY'S LOOKING FOR YOU.

I KNOW YOU! YOU'RE WHITEY!

YOU SAID I WAS SWELL-HEADED 'CAUSE I WAS A MOVIE STAR.

AW -- I DIDN'T MEAN NOTHIN'

AND THEN YOU KNOCKED ME DOWN AND GAVE ME A BLACK EYE.

AW -- I -

GOSH, WHITEY -- AM I **GLAD** TO SEE YOU?

5-7

NEXT WEEK -- CONTACTING MANDRAKE

CONTACTED BY WHITEY, MANDRAKE MEETS WITH SONNY'S KIDNAPPERS. BY A RUSE HE GETS SONNY AWAY FROM THEM, BUT THEY FOLLOW IN HOT PURSUIT!

MANDRAKE GESTURES---

PULL UP-- OR WE'LL SMASH YOU!

--AND HIS CAR SEEMS TO **JUMP RIGHT OVER** THE KIDNAPPERS' CAR....

5-9

MY--

--GOSH!

HIS CAR--**JUMPED** RIGHT OVER US! IT AIN'T POSSIBLE!

'COURSE, IT AIN'T! ANOTHER OF HIS TRICKS! WE'LL CATCH UP TO HIM!

WE'LL GET HIM NOW! OUR CAR'S HEAVIER! I'M GONNA CRASH INTO HIM! SAY--!

PETE! A STONE WALL-- IN THE MIDDLE OF THE ROAD! **PUT ON YOUR BRAKES!**

HIS CAR--JUST DISAPPEARED--!

I CAN STILL HEAR THE MOTOR RUNNING! IT'S RIGHT AHEAD OF US. ANOTHER ONE OF MANDRAKE'S TRICKS!

LOOK, THERE IT IS! REAPPEARED! HE STOPPED! I'M GOING TO GET HIM!

LOOK--BUD-- THOSE COPS --BLOCKING THE ROAD!

COPS NOTHING! JUST ANOTHER ONE OF THEM TRICKS! THEY'LL GO INTO THIN AIR, TOO, THE MINUTE WE GET THERE! I'M GONNA GIVE MANDRAKE A LOAD FROM THIS TOMMY-GUN!

5-12

YOU CAN'T KID ME AGAIN, MANDRAKE! THOSE AIN'T NO REAL COPS! JUST ANOTHER ONE OF YOUR TRICKS! NOW-- I'M GONNA GIVE YOU A LOAD OF THIS TOMMY-GUN!

5-13

I'LL EXPLAIN--BUT I MUST HURRY! THEY'VE FOLLOWED ME-- THEY'RE PROBABLY WATCHING ME RIGHT NOW!

YOU'RE A BIT UPSET. YOU'RE SAFE HERE. NO ONE'S WATCHING YOU.

5-17

BEFORE I BEGIN, YOU REALLY ARE MANDRAKE, AREN'T YOU? I MEAN, YOU HAVE SUPERNATURAL POWERS AND--

I SEE. YOU BREAK INTO MY HOUSE AND I MUST IDENTIFY MYSELF. WELL--

I WAS JUST SITTING DOWN TO READ--AH-- HERE COME MY BOOK AND SLIPPERS NOW!

AND NOW FOR A FIRE IN THE FIREPLACE--

5-18

THAT WAS MARVELOUS! YOU ARE MANDRAKE!

NOTHING SUPERNATURAL ABOUT IT. JUST A FEW SIMPLE TRICKS. NOW--WHO ARE YOU? YOUNG LADIES DON'T USUALLY COME INTO MY LIVINGROOM ON HORSE-BACK.

THE WILLOWS, ON BARKER ROAD -- DON'T FAIL ME! I NEED YOUR HELP!

IF THIS ISN'T THE STRANGEST BUSINESS! UNKNOWN GIRL ON HORSEBACK -- WILD TALE -- PANTHER FACE AT WINDOW -- IT'S LIKE A NIGHTMARE.

ME GOT BUMP ON KONK. REAL BUMP. NO NIGHTMARE.

5-20   *tomorrow* = THE WILLOWS

CAN YOU DIRECT ME TO THE WILLOWS?

THAT'S A BIG OLD HOUSE 'BOUT TWO MILE UP THE ROAD. SAY -- YOU AIN'T GOING THERE?

5-21

YES. WHO LIVES THERE?

NOBODY. IT'S BEEN EMPTY FOR YEARS. WHAT'S MORE -- IT'S HAUNTED!

BUT -- IF NOBODY LIVES IN HOUSE, WHO US GOING SEE WHEN GET THERE?

I DON'T KNOW. THIS SOUNDS INTERESTING.

INTERESTING? HUH -- NO USE -- GOING IN -- ALL EMPTY --

BUT WE HAVE TO GO IN, LOTHAR. WE'VE BEEN INVITED.

6 CONTINUED --

An UNKNOWN GIRL PLEADS WITH MANDRAKE TO HELP HER AND ASKS HIM TO COME TO HER HOUSE --THE WILLOWS.

SO THIS IS THE WILLOWS. NO LIGHTS --THE DOORBELL DOESN'T WORK --BUT THE DOOR IS OPEN. LET'S GO IN.

ME--ER-- PEACEFUL FELLA --NO LIKE GO LOOKING FOR TROUBLE!

5-23

HUH--SEE-- ALL EMPTY. US CAN GO NOW.

STOP ACTING LIKE A BABY, LOTHAR. THIS ISN'T A HAUNTED HOUSE-- BECAUSE THERE ARE NO SUCH THINGS AS "HAUNTS."

MUSTY OLD PLACE, THOUGH. I WONDER WHERE THE YOUNG LADY IS --- WHO'S THAT!

WHAT DO YOU WANT HERE?

AND MANDRAKE FACES THE BIGGEST WOMAN HE HAS EVER SEEN!....

WE WERE INVITED HERE BY THE YOUNG LADY WHO LIVES HERE. SHE SEEMED TO BE IN SOME SORT OF TROUBLE AND--

NO ONE HERE BUT ME. GET OUT.

5-24

THEN, FROM UPSTAIRS, COMES A VOICE....

NO. I WON'T!

Tomorrow = A WAY WITH THE LADIES

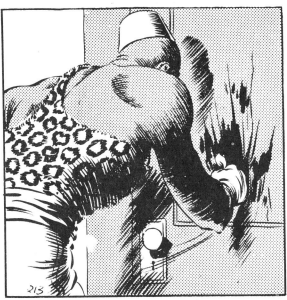

LOTHAR REACHES THRU *and* UNLOCKS THE DOOR.

MEANWHILE, IN ANOTHER PART OF THE HOUSE...

LILY BELL -- PUT ME DOWN!

NO!

THIS QUEER OLD HOUSE SEEMS TO BE EMPTY! WHAT HAPPENED TO ELLEN? SHE SEEMS TO HAVE VANISHED INTO THIN AIR!

THIN -- AIR! MAYBE -- GHOSTS TOOK HER --

NONSENSE, LOTHAR. YOU'VE SEEN FOR YOURSELF THAT THESE "GHOSTS" ARE JUST MECHANICAL GADGETS THAT --

6-4

FLOOR -- GOING --!

CONTINUED=

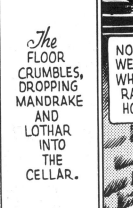

The FLOOR CRUMBLES, DROPPING MANDRAKE AND LOTHAR INTO THE CELLAR.

6-6

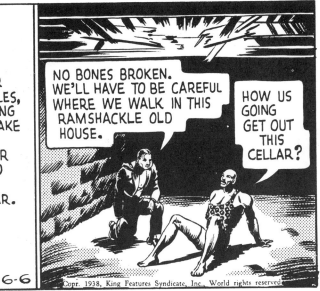

NO BONES BROKEN. WE'LL HAVE TO BE CAREFUL WHERE WE WALK IN THIS RAMSHACKLE OLD HOUSE.

HOW US GOING GET OUT THIS CELLAR?

WE'LL GET OUT THE WAY WE CAME IN.

BUT HOW ME GOING GET OUT? NO CAN CLIMB OUT ON OWN SHOULDERS!

OUR OLD LEVITATION TRICK STILL WORKS. HERE YOU COME, LOTHAR! NOW TO FIND ELLEN.

MANDRAKE GESTURES AND LOTHAR RISES ---

LOOK -- LADY MOUNTAIN, AGAIN!

A CHARMING LASS, WITH THE DISPOSITION OF A WOUNDED GORILLA. SHE'LL HAVE TO BE HANDLED WITH KID GLOVES.

tomorrow = MANDRAKE'S KID GLOVES!

PLEASE, LILY BELL, LET THEM IN. THEY'RE MY FRIENDS. YOU SEE, MANDRAKE, LILY BELL'S TRYING TO PROTECT ME. SHE DOESN'T TRUST ANYONE.

GO AWAY OR I'LL THROW YOU OUT OF THE HOUSE.

LILY BELL. A PERFECT NAME FOR SUCH A FRAGILE LITTLE WOMAN. I MUST GET HER AWAY SO I CAN TALK TO ELLEN, BUT AS LOTHAR SAYS, ONE CAN'T HIT A LADY, SO ---

ELLEN, DO YOU REMEMBER THE CHAIR THAT FLOATED IN THE AIR -- AND THE PIANO THAT PLAYED BY ITSELF -- AND THE PORTRAIT THAT TALKED?

YES!

THE CHAIR WAS PULLED THROUGH THE AIR BY WIRES AND THE PIANO AND THE PORTRAIT HAD MECHANICAL ATTACHMENTS TO MAKE THEM WORK. THAT'S WHAT YOUR "GHOSTS" REALLY WERE!

SO THAT'S IT!

DIDN'T YOU EVER INVESTIGATE THESE THINGS WHEN THEY HAPPENED?

NO -- OF COURSE NOT! I KNEW THE HOUSE WAS SUPPOSED TO BE HAUNTED. IT'S SUCH A GLOOMY OLD PLACE, ANYHOW. AS SOON AS ANYTHING HAPPENED -- I ALWAYS RAN -- TERRIFIED!

WELL, YOU KNOW NOW THAT THERE ARE NO SUCH THINGS AS GHOSTS. SOMEONE HAS BEEN TRYING TO SCARE YOU AND DOING A GOOD JOB OF IT, BUT ---

MANDRAKE! LOOK!

6-9

TOMORROW = THE GHOST

WOOOoooooo--

OH--!

MANDRAKE! IT'S THE CAT FACE!

SAME FELLA SOCKED ME ON KONK!

6-13
Copr 1938, King Features Syndicate, Inc., World rights reserved

ME GET!

LOTHAR CHASES THE CAT FACE THROUGH THE OLD HOUSE.

BUT THE CAT FACE IS FAST...

--AND AS HE OUT-DISTANCES HIS PURSUERS--

HIM SLIPPERY--AS GREASED CAT!

CAT FACE DODGES OUT OF LOTHAR'S GRASP---

ME SMACK HIM --IN JAW!

6-16

GOOD WORK, LOTHAR. THOSE FISTS OF YOURS CAN SETTLE ANY ARGUMENT. AND NOW WE SHALL SEE WHO CAT FACE IS!

tomorrow = SURPRISE

AND CAT FACE TURNS OUT TO BE---

DON! ELLEN'S FIANCE! SO YOU'RE THE CAT FACE GENTLEMAN WHO'S BEEN SCARING ELLEN OUT OF HER WITS! WHY?

LET ME--CATCH MY BREATH, MANDRAKE-- AND I'LL TELL YOU.

I LOVE ELLEN AND WE'RE GOING TO BE MARRIED. EVERYTHING WAS SWELL--UNTIL SHE GOT THIS INHERITANCE--WHICH WOULD MAKE HER A RICH WOMAN.

I'M POOR--BUT I'M NOT CUT OUT TO BE A GIGOLO I DIDN'T WANT TO BE SUPPORTED BY A RICH WIFE. I KNEW THAT ELLEN HAD TO LIVE IN THIS HOUSE A MONTH TO RECEIVE HER INHERITANCE.

6-17

THE HOUSE WAS SUPPOSED TO BE HAUNTED, ANYHOW--SO I TRIED TO SCARE ELLEN AWAY--SO SHE'D LOSE THE INHERITANCE. THEN, I'D WEAR THE PANTS IN THE FAMILY.

I DON'T ADMIRE YOUR METHODS, DON, BUT THERE'S SOMETHING IN WHAT YOU SAY.

TOMORROW= WHAT GHOST?

THE CAT FACE TURNS OUT TO BE DON, ELLEN'S FIANCE!

SO YOU ARRANGED THE TALKING PORTRAIT AND ALL THE OTHER GADGETS UPSTAIRS TO SCARE ELLEN OUT OF THE HOUSE, DON?

YES, I WANTED HER TO LOSE THE INHERITANCE, SO SHE'D HAVE TO LIVE ON MY INCOME. I'M NO GIGOLO!

6-18

AT LEAST, THAT SOLVES THE MYSTERY OF THIS "HAUNTED" HOUSE. YOU MADE A PRETTY EFFECTIVE GHOST, AT THAT.

GHOST? WHAT GHOST? YOU MEAN THIS PANTHER HEAD OUTFIT I WORE?

NO--I MEAN THE GHOST, COMPLETE WITH WHITE SHEET AND "WOOOOS".

BUT, MANDRAKE--I DIDN'T DO THAT! I WASN'T ANY GHOST. YOU MUST HAVE BEEN SEEING THINGS!

I WASN'T SEEING ANYTHING--ELLEN WAS STANDING WITH ME AND WE BOTH SAW---

MASTER! MISS ELLEN GONE--NO CAN FIND! HER DISAPPEARED!

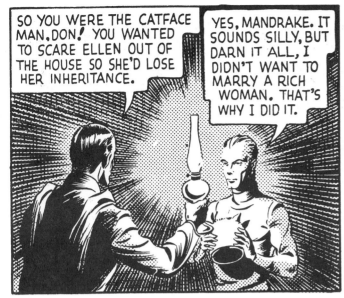

SO YOU WERE THE CATFACE MAN, DON! YOU WANTED TO SCARE ELLEN OUT OF THE HOUSE SO SHE'D LOSE HER INHERITANCE.

YES, MANDRAKE. IT SOUNDS SILLY, BUT DARN IT ALL, I DIDN'T WANT TO MARRY A RICH WOMAN. THAT'S WHY I DID IT.

NOW WE'VE GOT TO FIND ELLEN. YOU GO THAT WAY. I'LL GO THIS WAY.

ELLEN! WHAT DOES THIS MEAN!

MANDRAKE!

AS SHE SWINGS, MANDRAKE GESTURES -- THE AXE SEEMS TO SPROUT WINGS AS IT FLIES OUT OF HER HANDS! . . . .

MANDRAKE! I THOUGHT YOU WERE THE CATFACE MAN! I ALMOST HIT YOU! ---

ELLEN, ABOUT THE CATFACE MAN--

THE CATFACE MAN!

DON! YOU?

YES, SWEET.

6·21

--AND YOU TRIED TO SCARE ME AWAY, SO I'D LOSE THE FORTUNE, BECAUSE YOU DIDN'T WANT TO MARRY A RICH GIRL? OH, DON, I THINK THAT'S SO DARLING OF YOU!

tomorrow

THE UNINVITED GUEST

THERE'S STILL THAT "GHOST" TO BE ACCOUNTED FOR. ELLEN, IF YOU LOSE THE FORTUNE, WHO IS THE NEXT HEIR, ACCORDING TO THE WILL?

I'M THE ONLY HEIR. I MEAN, IF I LOSE IT, THE FORTUNE GOES TO SOME SCIENTIFIC RESEARCH INSTITUTE.

*HMM--*I HAD IMAGINED THAT WHO-EVER WAS TRYING TO GET YOU OUT OF THIS HOUSE WOULD INHERIT THE FORTUNE IF YOU LOST IT. THAT'S NOT THE CASE. WELL, --WHO WAS THE GHOST?

6·22

SUDDENLY, THERE IS A KNOCKING HEARD AT THE FRONT DOOR.

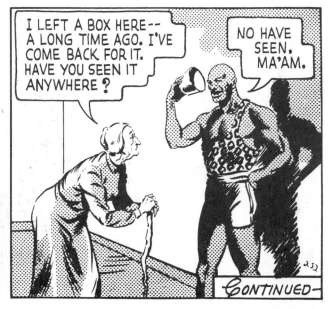

CONTINUED—

tomorrow = BY CANDLELIGHT

MANDRAKE IS ON THE TRAIL OF THE MYSTERIOUS OLD LADY WHO CALLS HERSELF MRS. WOODS.

AMAZING! THAT OLD LADY LOOKS EXACTLY LIKE THIS PORTRAIT, YET THE MRS. WOODS OF THIS PORTRAIT DIED IN 1908.

THE OLD LADY IS MRS. WOODS - SHE'S A--A GHOST!

HMM-- THESE PIECES OF CLAY IN FRONT OF THE PORTRAIT. IS IT POSSIBLE THAT--?

IS WHAT POSSIBLE?

I'LL TELL YOU LATER. SHE WENT THRU THAT TRAP-DOOR UPSTAIRS--SHE MUST BE IN THE CELLAR NOW.

AND IN THE CELLAR MANDRAKE SEES ---

6-30

MANDRAKE YOU MUSTN'T GO NEAR HER! SHE'S --A GHOST!

A PRETTY HEALTHY ONE, ELLEN. GHOSTS DON'T NEED TRAPDOORS TO GO THROUGH THE FLOOR.

AH--YOU HAVE COME TO HELP ME DIG?

YES, I'LL BE--

CONTINUED=

tomorrow = EXPLANATIONS

BUT DID YOU KNOW THIS MAN WAS WEARING A MASK, MANDRAKE?

NO, I GUESSED IT, AFTER I FOUND MOLDING CLAY ON THE FLOOR UNDER THE PORTRAIT. YOU SEE, IT LOOKS JUST LIKE THE PORTRAIT.

IN THE BAD LIGHT, IT WAS HARD TO NOTICE THE MASK. NOW-- WHY DID YOU MAKE THIS MASK--AND WHO ARE YOU?

BEFORE I TELL YOU, DO YOU MIND TELLING ME HOW YOU CHANGED INTO A SKELETON?

YOU MADE THE SHOVEL DIG BY ITSELF AND YOU MADE YOUR ARM AT LEAST FORTY FEET LONG! HOW?

DID I DO ALL THAT? COME, COME, YOU MUST HAVE BEEN **SEEING** THINGS!

The "GHOST" EXPLAINS...

I WAS CARETAKER FOR THIS HOUSE FOR YEARS, SEE? THEN THIS LADY INHERITS THE HOUSE! THE DAY I'M TO LEAVE, I DISCOVERS SOMETHING, SEE?

BUT IT'S TOO LATE FOR ME TO GET IT OUT OF THE HOUSE, SO I COMES BACK, SEE? I TRIES TO SCARE THE LADY OUT OF THE HOUSE.

WHAT DID YOU DISCOVER?

TOMORROW = MAKE THE BEST OF IT, DON

NEXT WEEK = NEW ADVENTURE

DATE DUE

GAYLORD   PRINTED IN U.S.A.